This book belongs to

_____

Publisher's Cataloging-in-Publication data

Names: Porter, Lee, 1956-, author. | Heinlein, Katelyn, illustrator.
Title: What do you feed a bat? / written by Lee Porter; illustrated by Katelyn Heinlein.
Description: Richmond, TX: Nana's Kids Books, 2023. | Summary: Fun and adventure with trying to find out
how to feed a bat. Trying food that is exotic and different to plain home down cooking.
Identifiers: LCCN: 2023912766 | ISBN: 978-1-7379252-3-1 (hardcover) | 978-1-7379252-4-8 (paperback)
978-1-7379252-5-5 (Kindle) | 979-8-9888700-0-5 (epub)
Subjects: LCSH Bats--Juvenile fiction. | Food--Juvenile fiction. | BISAC JUVENILE FICTION / General
Classification: LCC PZ7.1 .P67 Wh 2023 | DDC [E]--dc23

What Do You Feed A Bat?

Written by Lee Porter

Illustrated by Katelyn Heinlein

I have decided to invite
a bat for breakfast!
But what do bats eat anyway?

Will a bat eat **WAFFLES**
with fruit and a mountain
of whipped cream?

Or SCRAMBLED EGGS
with bacon and a side
of buttery toast?

I can serve him a
BOWL OF CEREAL–
or maybe a CHOCOLATE-covered
donut with colorful sprinkles.

If he can't make it
for breakfast,
how about brunch?

We can eat PANCAKES and BISCUITS—or "Ooh la la" French toast.

Should I be brave and invite my winged friend to a **TEA** room?

The Tea Room

We can wear fancy hats
and eat cucumber
SANDWICHES...

and drink tea with
our little pinkies up.

18

Do bats like **SUSHI**, or will the fishy smell bother him?

Maybe I'll invite him for a
PICNIC with beans,
potato salad, and watermelon.

I quite like **SPAGHETTI**,
but will my bat friend get too messy?

We can go to the **THEATER** that serves lunch. Maybe he will be too busy to even notice what he is eating.

MEXICAN food is full of hot spices, but will that be too much?

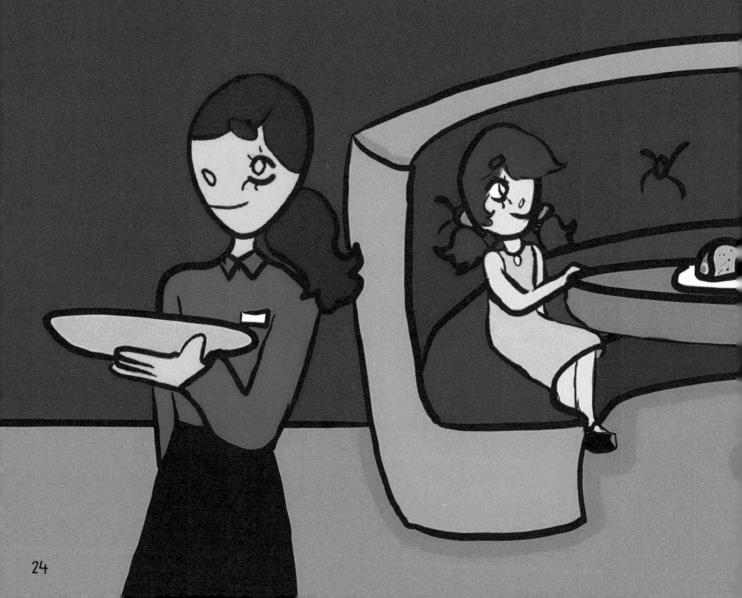

Maybe I'll serve him
a taco and a quesadilla.

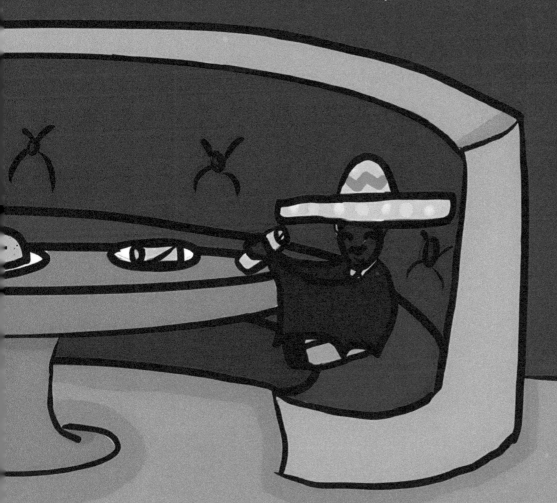

Or a **GYRO** with
a side of fries.
That sounds Greek to me!

What? Oh no! Did you say bats
don't wake up till
DINNER TIME?

That's no problem!
I'll just invite him for dinner.

Oh dear, what do bats eat for dinner?

Author

Lee Porter was on her usual walk when she attracted some new walking companions—bats! Why were bats following her? She turned to her grandchildren for help. Her grandson Austin helped sort out the true facts about bats, while her granddaughter Katelyn came up with the adorable illustrations for the book. They never knew that bats would become such an interesting family project.

Illustrator

Katelyn Heinlein is a creative young artist who illustrated this book in the midst of the pandemic. She is a high school student who loves reading and dance and has performed leaps and pirouettes to expertly make the words of the book come to life.

I hope you enjoyed
the book.

Please leave us a review.

www.bit.ly/whatdoyoufeedabat-review

Interesting Facts About Bats

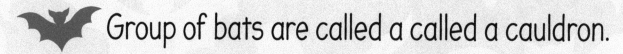 Group of bats are called a called a cauldron.

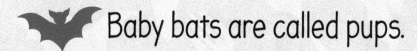 Baby bats are called pups.

 Bats can eat 1,200 mosquitoes an hour.

 They can live more than 30 years.

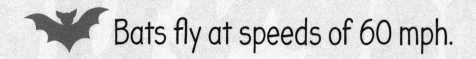 Bats fly at speeds of 60 mph.

They can't stand upright and this is why they hang upside down.

They are nocturnal and come out at night.

They eat beetles, flies, moths, fruit, fish (at least one) and even blood.

Not all bats hibernate in the winter.

 Bats have few natural predators.

 Bats are the only mammals that truly fly.

 Vampire bats feed entirely on blood.

 The largest bats have a six foot wing span.

 The smallest bat, is known as the bumblebee bat and is less than 1.4 inches, with a body the size of a dime.

 There are more than 1400 species of bats.